Mastering the Classical Guitar

Book 1A

By Wissam Abboud

To access the online audio go to:
WWW.MELBAY.COM/30683MEB

Acknowledgments

I would like to thank my family, friends and teachers for the continuous help, support, positive thoughts, and love that they provided me. You are all a real source of inspiration!

Moreover, I would like to thank my students who have been part of this book's gradual development over the last few years. I hope that I inspired you as much as you have inspired me!

Design by **Yara Bou Karam**
Photography by **Pierre & Pia Bou Karam**

Table of Contents

Acknowledgments 2
Table of Contents 3
About the Author 4
About this Book 4
How to Use this Book 5
A Note to Students 5
Recommendations 5

The Classical Guitar 6
Tuning 6
Playing Position 7
Fingers 8
Right-Hand Position 9
Strokes 10
Left-Hand Position 11

Part I: Progressive Studies and Pieces

Chapter I: Basic Music Symbols 12
Pitch Notation 12
Rhythmic Notation 13

Chapter II: The Right Hand 14
Open Strings 1, 2, & 3 14
Combining Open Strings 15

Chapter III: The Left Hand 16
Notes on the First String 16
Notes on the Second String 17
Combining Strings 1 & 2 18
First Songs 19
Notes on the Third String 21

Chapter IV: Rhythm Studies 23
Eighth Notes 23
Rests 25
Pickup Notes 26
Ties 29
Dotted Quarter Notes 30

Chapter V: The Thumb 32
The Open Bass Strings 32
Combining Bass Strings 32
Notes on the Fourth String 33
Notes on the Fifth String 35

**Chapter VI: Accidentals
& Key Signatures** 37
Sharps, Flats and Natural Signs 37
Key Signatures 40

**Chapter VII: Using all the Notes
of the First Position** 41
Notes on the Sixth String 41

**Chapter VIII: Combining Right
Hand Fingers** 45
Combining Thumb and Fingers 45
Music in Two Parts 46

Chapter IX: Right-Hand Development 50
Notes Played Together 50

Chapter X: 6/8 Time Signature 55
6/8 Time Signature 55
Arpeggios with *p-i-m* 59

Part II: Technical Exercises 60

Part III: Rhythmic Reading 67

Appendix 70

Practicing 70
Sight Reading 70
Memorization 71
Guitar Care 71

About the Author

Wissam Abboud is an accomplished Lebanese guitarist, composer and instructor who always strives for perfection. He graduated from Notre Dame University-Louaize (NDU) with a Bachelor of Arts and a Master of Arts in Musicology. He also earned a Bachelor of Arts in Music - Classical Guitar Performance and Baccalaureate Diplomas in Theoretical Studies and Sight Singing from the Lebanese National Higher Conservatory of Music.

Wissam is also the co-author of the book entitled **"Acoustic Duo"**, an instrumental songbook for guitar duo composed by Wissam and Roy Abboud.

After many years of teaching classical guitar and knowing the detailed obstacles that students usually suffer from regardless of the method used, Wissam felt the need for a different approach. He began to write specific exercises for his students to help them overcome their difficulties, then after a few years, decided to incorporate them in a new classical guitar method series.

Wissam is currently a Guitar, Theory and Sight Singing instructor at the School of Music of Antonine and Notre Dame Universities.

For more information about Wissam Abboud and his music please visit: *Wissam Abboud*
www.WissamAbboud.com

About this Book

This publication is the first in a progressive series using a wide variety of musical repertoire and educational material to provide a solid technical foundation for classical guitar students, exposing the full range of the instrument's potential and repertoire.

Book 1A is most appropriate for students with no prior knowledge of the guitar or music theory, or for those who simply want a fresh start with the classic guitar. It is written in three broad sections: **Progressive Studies and Pieces, Technical Exercises** and **Rhythmic Reading**. Tips on how to integrate the three sections are provided throughout the book. Every chapter begins with exercises written specifically to improve a certain aspect of ones playing, followed by various examples from the classical music repertoire and traditional songs from various cultures. While every aspect of classical guitar technique is clearly described and illustrated, students using this book would still benefit from the advice and constructive feedback of a competent teacher. Consequently, teachers will find opportunities to assert their individual teaching perspectives within this method, making it a perfect roadmap for the instructor and student's musical journey.

This book is written in standard notation only and comes with extensive online audio examples. Fingering is kept to a minimum to encourage effective sight reading.

How to Use this Book

- **Find a good teacher.** While this publication can be used for self-instruction, it is intended for use under the supervision of a qualified teacher. Many concepts have been left out to allow a degree of flexibility in teaching styles.

- **There are three sections in this book**: Progressive Studies and Pieces, Technical Exercises, and Rhythmic Reading. It is recommended that you work on the three sections simultaneously. Tips on how to integrate the three sections are throughout the book.

- **Do not skip lessons**; try to address each page sequentially whenever possible.

- **Avoid adding excessive left-hand fingering**. Fingering markings have been kept to a minimum in this book as reading music without fingering is very beneficial.

- Before playing any study or piece, **look at the complete line of music**, read the notes, and pay attention to the time signature, key signature, and rhythm.

- **Always count the beats.** In the first few lessons, it is recommended to count the rhythm aloud; later on, keep counting it in your head without tapping your foot.

- **Use additional material.** No beginner's book will satisfy all of your personal interests and needs, so request further materials from your teacher as needed. Additional resources are available at **www.WissamAbboud.com**

- Passages that are marked with a ⌐dashed box⌐ require special attention. It is recommended to practice these passages 10 times or more until you master them; then proceed to practice the rest of the piece.

A Note to Students

- Practice at least half an hour per day on a regular basis.
- It's all about quality not quantity.
- Use good playing posture.
- Use a metronome.
- Follow the indicated fingering.
- Listen to your teacher.
- Always tune your guitar properly before playing.

Recommended Books while Using this Method

- Sight Reading for Guitarists (Marsh)/Mel Bay Publications, Inc.

Recommended Books after Completion of this Method

- Mastering the Classical Guitar, Book 1B, by Wissam Abboud/Mel Bay Publications, Inc.
- Complete Carcassi Guitar Method/Mel Bay Publications, Inc.
- Aaron Shearer Learning the Classical Guitar Part 1/Mel Bay Publications, Inc.
- Aaron Shearer Learning the Classical Guitar Part 2/Mel Bay Publications, Inc.

The Classical Guitar

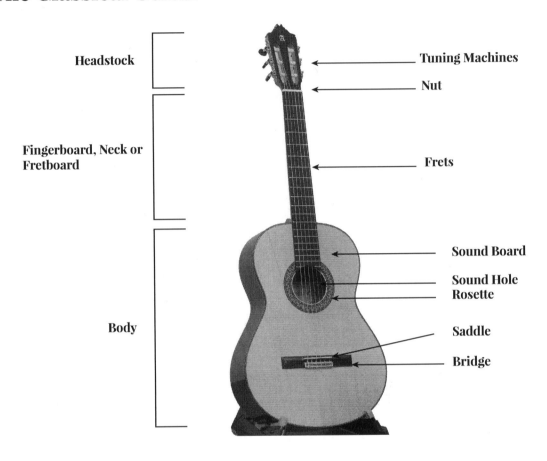

Headstock

Fingerboard, Neck or Fretboard

Body

Tuning Machines

Nut

Frets

Sound Board

Sound Hole
Rosette

Saddle

Bridge

Tuning

Guitar Strings (from low to high)

E	A	D	G	B	E
Mi	**La**	**Ré**	**Sol**	**Si**	**Mi**
6	**5**	**4**	**3**	**2**	**1**

Always make sure to tune your guitar properly before playing!

There are many ways to tune the guitar. Advanced musicians can easily tune their instruments by ear, but this talent is acquired over time and many years of practice. Until you develop this musical ability, it is recommended to use an electronic tuner. Electronic tuners are quick, precise and easy to use. When a note is played, the tuner determines the note, then represents visually how sharp or flat it is. Tuning machines are used to adjust the pitch of each string.

Make sure you are turning the correct knob for the string you are trying to tune.

Tuners are also available to download as mobile apps, and most of them are free!

Playing Position

Sitting Position with a Footstool

Sitting Position with a Guitar Support

Sitting Position

- Use a normal height armless chair.
- Sit squarely, and as forward on the chair as possible.
- Legs should be bent at 90 degree angles at the knees.
- Feet should be flat on the floor, and the back should be straight.
- Shoulders should be relaxed.
- Unnecessary body tension should be avoided.

Holding the Guitar

- The guitar should be placed on the left leg, and supported by the right leg.
- The right arm should rest lightly against the edge of the guitar.
- The headstock of the guitar should be approximately at eye level.
- The fingerboard should be tilted slightly upward.
- Lean slightly forward to better see the fretboard.
- In a correct position, there should be no need to support the neck with the left hand.
- The guitar must be held in a very stable position. A footstool or guitar support is recommended to position the guitar in a way that compliments your body posture.

Sitting Position   Sitting Position *(side view)*

Fingers

In **Classical Guitar**, the fingers of the right hand are designated by the letters *p, i, m,* and *a,* which are abbreviations of their Spanish names, and the left-hand fingers are designated by the numbers **1, 2, 3** and **4**, starting from the index.

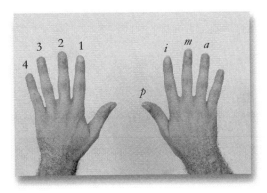

Fingers

p = thumb *(pulgar)*

i = index *(índice)*

m = middle *(medio)*

a = ring *(anular)*

Note: The left-hand nails should be kept short enough so that they do not strike the strings or fretboard. It is not recommended for beginners to use their right-hand nails while playing the guitar.

The Right Hand

- The right hand should be placed over the lower third of the sound hole.
- The wrist should be more or less flat, or slightly arched.
- The thumb should be relaxed, hanging downward in a natural position without touching the body of the guitar or the strings. In rare cases, you can rest your thumb on the 6th string or another bass string, but this might lead to a bad habit.
- As a starting position, place the tip of your fingers on the treble (nylon) strings.
- Your wrist should be 2 – 3 inches from the top of the guitar.
- Keep your shoulders relaxed.
- Use a mirror so you can see exactly how your hand is positioned while you play.
- The strings must be struck using your fingertips.

Right-Hand Position (*side view*)

Right-Hand Position

To position the right hand correctly, form a fist and rest it on the strings facing the sound hole as showed in the illustration below; then, loosen the fist and push up with your fingers slowly to open your hand. Place your thumb on the 6th string and the other fingers on the first three strings.

Right-Hand Position (*with a formed fist*)

Right-Hand Position

Strokes

Rest Stroke

Rest-Stroke (*preparation*)

Rest-Stroke (*completion*)

The **rest stroke** is a method of plucking the strings. After playing a rest stroke on a string, the finger comes to rest against the adjacent string. The string must be struck inwards towards the body of the guitar to produce a full and round sound.

Rest stroke is usually used in parts that require special emphasis, such as melodies in two-part music (melody and accompaniment), or scales.

Free Stroke

Free-Stroke (*preparation*)

Free-Stroke (*completion*)

The **free stroke** is a method of plucking the strings. After playing a free stroke on a string, the finger swings freely above the adjacent string. The first part of the movement is exactly like the rest stroke (the string is struck inwards towards the body of the guitar, but never upward). The difference is that free stroke involves a slight lifting of the tip joint of the finger after stroking the note to avoid resting on the adjacent string.

Free stroke is usually used while playing arpeggios, chords, passages where rest stroke is not practical, and parts which do not require special emphasis.

Tip: It is recommended to use both types of strokes from the early stages of learning. The choice of either starting with rest stroke or free stroke is left up to the teacher, depending on the ability and ease of playing of each student.

The Left Hand

- The left arm should be relaxed.
- The left hand plays no part in supporting the guitar or maintaining its position.
- The thumb supports the playing position, and should be placed at the center of the back of the neck.
- The palm should be parallel to the fingerboard.
- Knuckles should also be parallel to the fingerboard.
- Fingers should always be curved at both joints.
- The nails of the left hand must be very short.
- Press the strings down using the fingertips.
- Apply the minimum pressure needed to produce a clear tone.

Practice the left-hand position by placing the four fingers on the fingerboard, with each finger on a different fret.
Make sure to place the tips of your fingers immediately behind the frets.

Left-Hand Position (*side view*)

Left-Hand Position (*top view*)

Left-Hand Position

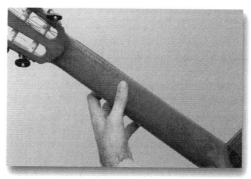

Position of the Thumb

Part I: Progressive Studies and Pieces
Chapter I: Basic Music Symbols
Pitch Notation

1 **Note Names:**

C   D   E   F   G   A   B
Do Ré Mi Fa Sol La Si

2 **The Staff:** The *staff* is the foundation upon which notes are drawn. It is comprised of five lines and four spaces.

3 **Treble Clef:** Clefs assign individual notes to certain lines or spaces. In classical guitar, the treble clef is used to indicate the names of the notes.

Notes can be written on lines, spaces and ledger lines (4, 5 & 6)

4 **Lines:**

E   G   B   D   F

5 **Spaces:**

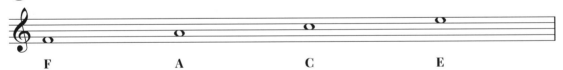

F   A   C   E

6 **Ledger Lines:** Notes above or below the staff are written on additional lines called *ledger lines.*

7 **The Octave:** The interval between a higher and lower note of the same name is called an *octave.*

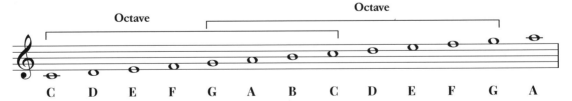

C   D   E   F   G   A   B   C   D   E   F   G   A

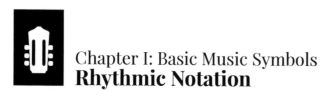

Chapter I: Basic Music Symbols
Rhythmic Notation

8 **Values of Notes:**

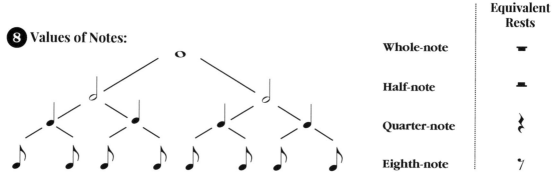

	Equivalent Rests
Whole-note	▬
Half-note	▬
Quarter-note	𝄽
Eighth-note	𝄾

9 **Bars and Measures:**

The staff is divided into measures by bar lines.

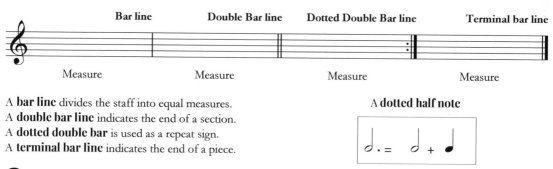

A **bar line** divides the staff into equal measures.
A **double bar line** indicates the end of a section.
A **dotted double bar** is used as a repeat sign.
A **terminal bar line** indicates the end of a piece.

A dotted half note

$$\text{♩·} = \text{♩} + \text{♩}$$

10 **Time Signatures:**

The upper number shows the number of beats in each measure.
The lower number shows the kind of note which receives one beat.

two beats to a measure

a quarter note gets **one beat**

three beats to a measure

a quarter note gets **one beat**

Four beats to a measure

a quarter note gets **one beat**

Six beats to a measure (divided into two groups of three)

an eighth note gets **one beat**

11 **Counting the Beat:**

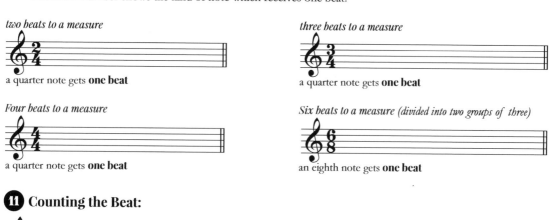

Count : 1 2 3 4   1 2 3 4   1 2 3 4   1 & 2 & 3 & 4 &

Chapter II: The Right Hand
Open Strings 1, 2 & 3

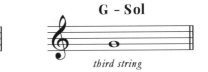

Always alternate between *i* and *m* fingers.

First String - E (Mi)

Second String - B (Si)

Count the beats aloud as you play.

Third String - G (Sol)

Chapter II: The Right Hand
Combining Open Strings

You can also start with the *m* finger.

Read all the notes aloud before you play.

Alternate between *i* and *m*.

Count the beats aloud as you play.

Chapter III: The Left Hand
Notes on the First String

E - Mi

open string

F - Fa

1st fret
1st finger

G - Sol

3rd fret
3rd finger

Practice these four exercises to get used to the new position. Repeat as many times as needed!
Place only the fingertips on the strings *(Review p.11)*.

Read all the notes aoud before you play.

Chapter III: The Left Hand
Notes on the Second String

Notice the 3/4 time signature below.

Count the beats aloud as you play.

Chapter III: The Left Hand
Combining Strings 1 & 2

Read all the notes aloud before you play. Practice slowly, then gradually increase the tempo (speed).

Upon completion of this exercise, start practicing numbers 1-5 from the Technical Exercises on p. 60.

Play slowly and evenly.

Chapter III: The Left Hand
First Songs

Try playing with both rest stroke and free stroke.

Ode to Joy (from *Symphony 9*) — Beethoven (1770 - 1827)

Sur le Pont d'Avignon — France

"C" means *common time*, it is the same as 4/4.

Lightly Row — Germany

Trallerliedchen (from *Album for the Young*) — Schumann (1810 - 1856)

Try to keep your eyes on the music as much as possible; train the fingers to find their way.

J'ai du Bon Tabac

France

Da Capo al Fine, often abbreviated as **D.C. al Fine**, is an Italian term that means go back to the beginning (capo) and play to the **Fine** (end) sign.

Jingle Bells

Christmas Carol

Chapter III: The Left Hand
Notes on the Third String

G - Sol

open string

A - La

2nd fret
2nd finger

i m i m
Count : 1 2 3 4

Old MacDonald Had a Farm   Traditional

i m i m
Count : 1 2 3 4

Yankee Doodle   Traditional

i m i m
Count : 1 2 3 4

Upon completion of this piece, start practicing number 6 from the Technical Exercises on p. 60.

Mary Had a Little Lamb   Traditional

m i m i
Count : 1 2 3 4

10 **Twinkle, Twinkle Little Star**

France
Fine

Count : 1 2 3 4

D.C. al Fine

11 **Au Clair de la Lune**

France

Count : 1 2 3 4

12 **Andantino**

Schubert (1797 - 1828)

Count : 1 2 3 4

Chapter IV: Rhythm Studies
Eighth Notes

An **eighth note** is half the length of a quarter note.
When counting eighth notes, continue to count quarter notes as downbeats, and say the word "and" on the upbeats.

Upon completion of this exercise, start practicing numbers 7-9 from the Technical Exercises on p. 61.

Notice the 2/4 time signature below. Count aloud as you play.

J'ai du Bon Tabac   France

Good King Wenceslas   Christmas Carol

Clarita is my guitar student. She completed her first opus when she was 12!

15 Running Under the Sun *(Opus 1, No. 4)*   Clarita Youakim (2005)

© Copyright 2017 Clarita Youakim. Used by permission.

16 Ecossaise   Wissam Abboud (1993)

17 Minuet   W. A. Mozart (1756 - 1791)

18 Frère Jacques   France

Chapter IV: Rhythm Studies
Rests

A **rest** is a symbol for a musical silence. It shows when not to play or when to mute a ringing note.

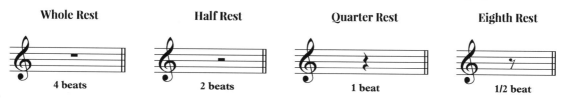

Whole Rest	Half Rest	Quarter Rest	Eighth Rest
4 beats	2 beats	1 beat	1/2 beat

A **whole rest** indicates a **complete measure of silence** in any time signature.

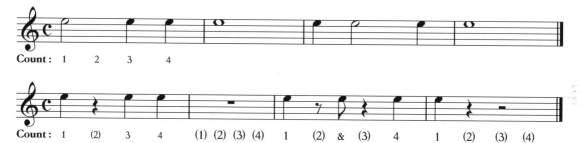

Count : 1   2   3   4

Count : 1 (2) 3 4   (1) (2) (3) (4)   1 (2) & (3) 4   1 (2) (3) (4)

Naya is my guitar student and an aspiring composer. This is one of her first compositions; she wrote it when she was 10!

Chanson de Bonheur

Naya Whaibé (2006)

Count : 1   &   2   &   3   &   4   &

Pickup Notes

When the first bar starts with a rest(s), the rest can be omitted, creating what we call a *pickup note*(s), or *anacrusis*.

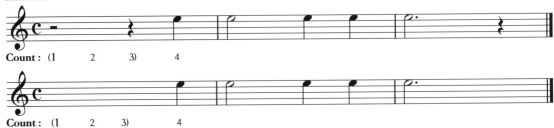

To make up for the missing rests at the start of a pickup bar, the final bar **often** leaves out the number of beats that are present in the pickup bar. Together, the total number of beats in the pickup bar and the final bar add up to one whole bar.

L'Apprenti Pastouriau

Traditional

Count aloud as you play.

Bingo

Traditional

When **first & second endings** are used, play the music once including the first ending, then repeat the music again but this time skip the first ending and go directly to the second ending.

24 Santiano

France

Count :   4   &   1   &   2   &   3   &   4   &

25 We Wish You a Merry Christmas

Christmas Carol

Count :   3   &   1   &   2   &   3   &

Fine

1   2

3

D.C. al Fine

Chapter IV: Rhythm Studies
Ties

A **tie** joins two notes of the same pitch. The first note is played and held for the value of two notes without playing the second one.

When the Saints Go Marching In

Traditional

Chapter IV: Rhythm Studies
Dotted Quarter Notes

A **dot** placed after a note increases the time value of the note by one-half. A **dotted quarter note** has a value equal to a quarter note plus an eighth note.

Notice that measures 2 & 3 sound the same

Count: 1 & 2 & 3 & 4 & 1 & 2 & 3 & 4 & 1 & 2 & 3 & 4 &

Count: 1 & 2 & 3 & 4 & 1 & 2 & 3 & 4 & 1 & 2 & 3 & 4 &

27 Alouette   Traditional

Count: 1 & 2 & 3 & 4 &   1 & 2 & 3 & 4 &

Upon completion of this piece, start practicing number 10 from the Technical Exercises on p. 61.

28 Deck the Halls   Christmas Carol

Count: 1 & 2 & 3 & 4 &   1 & 2 & 3 & 4 &

29 Cockles and Mussels   Ireland

Count: 3   1 & 2 & 3 & 1 &

Count aloud as you play.

Etude (30)

Wissam Abboud (1993)

Count: 1 & 2 & 3 & 1 & 2 & 3 &

Etude (31)

Wissam Abboud (1993)

Count: 1 & 2 & 3 & 4 &

Calleno Costure Me (32)

Anon.

Count: 1   2   3   1 & 2 & 3

Ce n'est qu'un au Revoir/Auld Lang Syne (33)

Scotland

Count: 4 & 1 & 2 & 3 & 4 &

Chapter V: The Thumb
The Open Bass Strings

The bass strings are usually played using the thumb. Keep your thumb relaxed and play using free stokes.

Fourth String - D (Ré)

Fifth String - A (La)

Sixth String - E (Mi)

Combining Bass Strings

Chapter V: The Thumb
Notes on the Fourth String

Practice these four exercises to get used to the new position.

When a bass-note melody reaches the third string, you can use the thumb to play it.

Count aloud as you play.

In the following example, the first section can be played using *p*, and the second section using *i-m*.

34 Andantino   Wissam Abboud (1993)

When a melody uses several strings, it can be played using *i-m*.

35 He is Born, The Divine Child   Christmas Carol

36 Peasant Costume (*Romanian Folk Dance No. 2*)   Béla Bartók (1881 - 1945)

Chapter V: The Thumb
Notes on the Fifth String

A - La

open string

B - Si

2ⁿᵈ fret
2ⁿᵈ finger

C - Do

3ʳᵈ fret
3ʳᵈ finger

Practice these four exercises to get used to the new position.

1)   2)   3)   4)

Symphony 1 *(Frère Jacques Theme)*

Gustav Mahler (1860 - 1911)

Upon completion of this piece, start practicing numbers 11-13 from the Technical Exercises on p. 62-63.

Etude

Wissam Abboud (1993)

Toccata

J. S. Bach (1685 - 1750)

Theme from "New World Symphony"

A. Dvořák (1841 - 1904)

Atoye

Anon.

Asturias *(Leyenda)*

I. Albeniz (1860 - 1909)

Chapter VI: Accidentals & Key Signatures
Sharps, Flats and Natural Signs

Sharps, **flats** and **natural** signs are used to alter a note by raising or lowering it by one half-step, which is equal to one fret on the guitar. The effects of these alterations last for only one measure. These signs are also called *accidentals*. Notes that have different names but sound the same are called *enharmonics*.

Note: From this point on, it is recommended to continue in conjunction with **Chapter VIII.**

When a note of an open string is **sharped**, it is played on the first fret of the same string.
When a note of an open string is **flatted**, it is played on the lower adjacent string.

G-Sharp

3rd string
1st fret, 1st finger

B-Flat

3rd string
3rd fret, 3rd finger

Romanze *(from Eine Kleine Nachtmusic, K 525)*   W. A. Mozart (1756 - 1791)

Andante   W. A. Mozart (1756 - 1791)

Fine

D.C. al Fine

La Ci Darem la Mano *(from Don Giovanni)*

W. A. Mozart (1756 - 1791)

Fine

D.C. al Fine

Für Elise

Beethoven (1770 - 1827)

Chapter VI: Accidentals & Key Signatures
Key Signatures

A **Key signature** is used to indicate altered notes throughout an entire piece. These are examples of key signatures that will be used throughout this book.

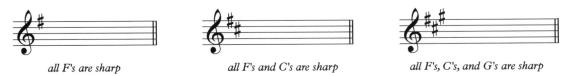

all F's are sharp   *all F's and C's are sharp*   *all F's, C's, and G's are sharp*

Pay attention to the left-hand fingering when playing in new keys.

Key of G Major

Key of D Major

Key of A Major

Bourrée (from *Lute Suite in E minor, BWV 996)*   J. S. Bach (1685 - 1750)

Chapter VII: Using all the Notes of the First Position
Notes on the Sixth String

E - Mi
open string

F - Fa
1st fret
1st finger

G - Sol
3rd fret
3rd finger

49 **Fandango**   Wissam Abboud (1993)

Upon completion of this piece, start practicing numbers 14-18 from the Technical Exercises on p. 63-64-65.

50 **Allegro**   Wissam Abboud (1993)

Etude 1 *(Op. 60)*   Fernando Sor (1778 - 1839)

In the Hall of the Mountain King (from *Peer Gynt Suite)*   E. Grieg (1843 - 1907)

Etude 3 *(Op. 60)*   Fernando Sor (1778 - 1839)

Minuet in G   J. S. Bach (1685 - 1750)

Chapter VIII: Combining Right Hand Fingers
Combining Thumb and Fingers

Pay attention to your right-hand position. Before playing the next exercises, place your *i*, *m* and *a* fingers on the first three strings, and the thumb on any of the bass strings. This is the position that should be used while playing. Don't change the position while playing treble or bass strings.

Upon completion this exercise, start practicing number 19 from the Technical Exercises on p. 66.

56 Dance

Wissam Abboud (1993)

57 Memories

Wissam Abboud (1993)

Chapter VIII: Combining Right Hand Fingers
Music in Two Parts

From this lesson onward, we will deal with music in two parts, which consists of a melody and a bass accompaniment. To avoid confusion and error, start by playing the melody, then play both the melody and bass together.

Divertissement

A. Cano-Curriella (1811-1897)

Waltz

Wissam Abboud (1993)

Play the melody only at first; then add the bass line.

Minuet Wissam Abboud (1993)

Fine

D.C. al Fine

Nostalgia Wissam Abboud (1993)

Pay attention to the key signature and the fingering.

Minuet

Wissam Abboud (1993)

Dance

Wissam Abboud (1993)

Again, play the melody only at first; then add the bass line.

Autumn Waltz [64]

Lyse Gingras (1949)

Chapter IX: Right Hand Development
Notes Played Together

The following exercise is an example of two notes played simultaneously. Practice the example slowly until you can play it with ease before playing the next pieces.

Ricercar

Anon.

Upon completion of this piece, start practicing number 20 from the Technical Exercises on p. 66.

Siciliani

M. Carcassi (1792 - 1853)

67 **Waltz**

Anon.

68 **Quand J'étais Chez mon Père**

France

Hymn

J. A. P. Schultz (1747-1800)

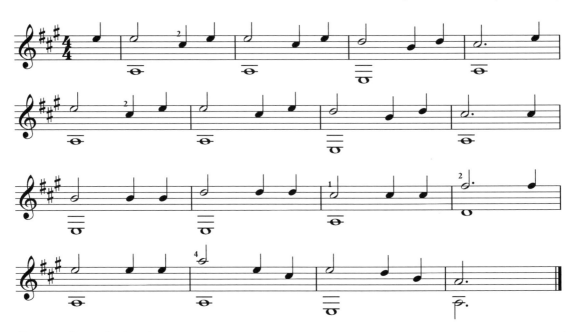

Pay attention to the key signature.

Savez-vous Planter les Choux?

France

Spanish Dance

Wissam Abboud (1993)

Danse d'Avila

Anon.

Carrousel

Claude Gagnon

Chapter X: 6/8 Time Signature
6/8 Time Signature

In **6/8 Time Signature**, each eighth note gets one count (equal to one beat), thus a quarter note gets two beats, and a dotted quarter note gets three beats. 6/8 time signature is felt in two groups of three.

Count : 1 2 3 4 5 6   1 2 3 4 5 6

74 Theme from Sonata 15

N. Paganini (1782 - 1840)

Count : 4 5 6   1 2 3 4 5 6   1 2 3 4 5 6

Upon completion of this piece, start practicing number 21 from the Technical Exercises on p. 66.

75 Fais Dodo

France

Romance

Anon.

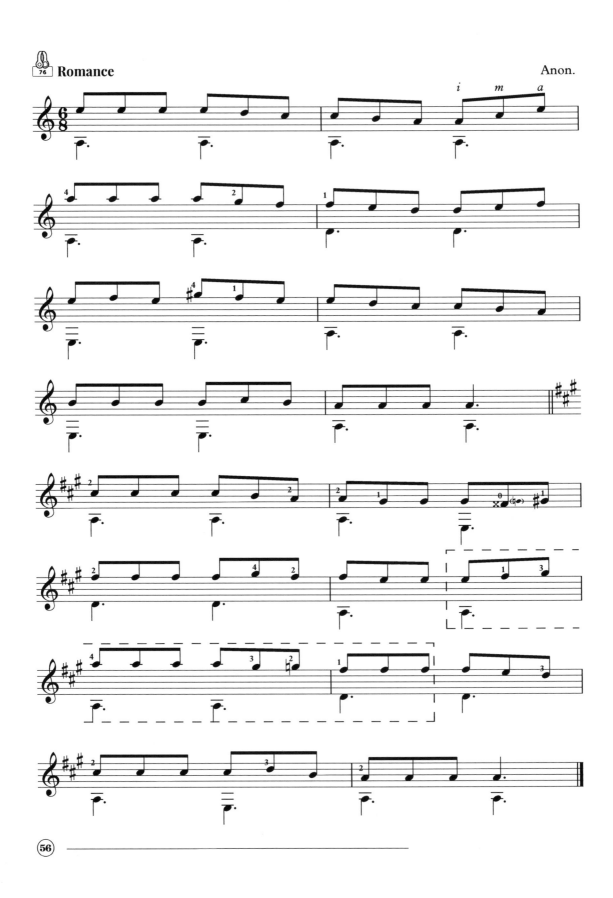

78 **Moderato** *(Op. 39, No. 15)* — Anton Diabelli (1781-1858)

79 **Fanfare** — Wissam Abboud (1993)

Chapter X: 6/8 Time Signature
Arpeggios with *p-i-m*

There are a lot of different finger combinations that create arpeggios. These combinations will be covered in the next book in this series, but for now, we will start with three-string arpeggios: the *p-i-m*.

 **Atmosphere**

Wissam Abboud (1993)

Part II: Technical Exercises

Playing these technical exercises on a **daily basis** will help you build accuracy, synchronization, facility. Using a metronome, begin slowly and increase the speed gradually.

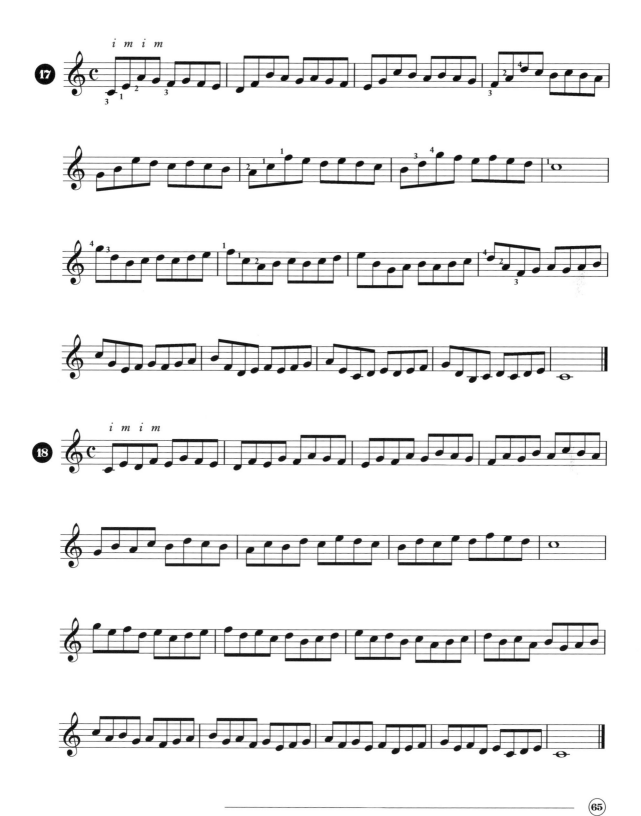

Part III: Rhythmic Reading

Clap or play on an open string the following rhythmic exercises. **Be sure to count aloud!**

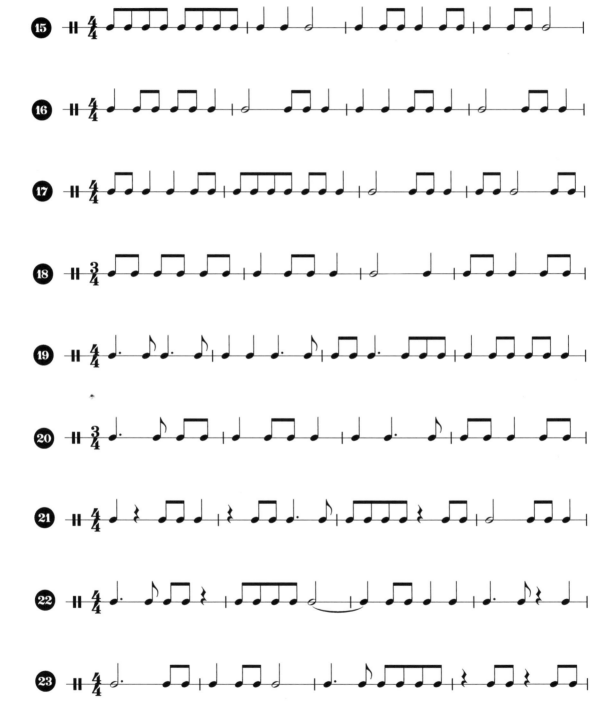

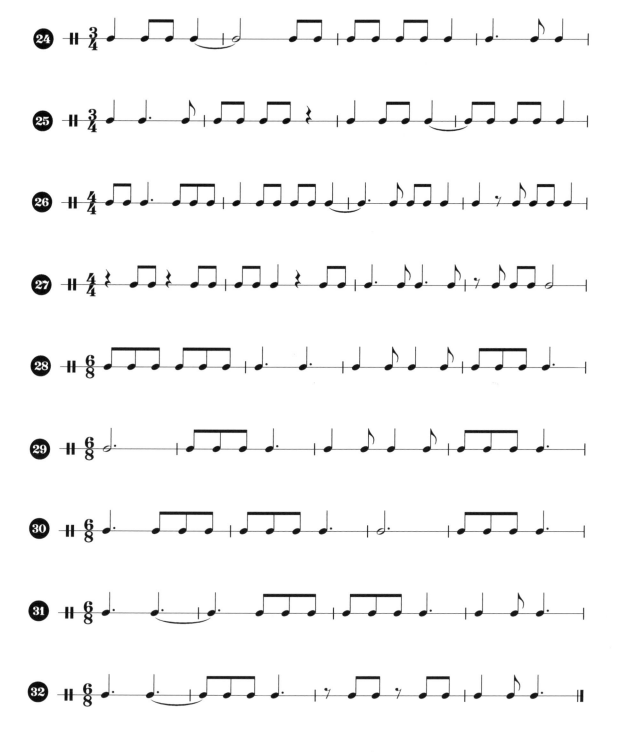

Appendix

Practicing

There are many factors that can affect the quality of your practice, such as the level of difficulty, the amount of material addressed, practice time, and tempo.

Practice is not only about repetition. If you repeat a piece 50 times incorrectly, do you expect to get it right on the 51st time? Probably not! Unless you change your practice approach, you will not get it right.

Practicing approach should be focused on problem solving more than robotic repetition.
Every piece presents different challenges, but in all cases the approach is almost the same. First of all, you should identify the problems, and understand their exact cause. Knowing and understanding the problems is the key to solving them.
The most effective way to solve these problems is the technique of spotting, which includes:
Identification, Microscopic Practice, and **Assimilation**.

❶ Identification: Find the trouble spot(s) and mark them with a pencil. These could be a few measures long, one measure long, or even shorter.

❷ Microscopic Practice: Practice the identified section(s) and repeat them as an interrupted exercise for a few minutes while focusing on every note and hand movement. Using a metronome, start with a very slow tempo and increase it gradually to reach the desired tempo.

❸ Assimilation: Assemble the phrases and passages that were practiced separately, putting them back in context, and adding a few bars before and after the specific spot, until the whole piece can be played seamlessly.

Sight Reading

Sight reading is one of the most important skills a musician can develop, but classical guitarists often neglect it. It is true that sight reading is sometimes difficult on the guitar, because the exact same notes can be played in many positions and on different strings; that's the reason why it is important to develop facility in sight reading. The best way to approach it is to incorporate it in your daily practice routine from the early stages of learning the instrument. It also helps to play in a small ensemble of players with similar abilities.

Tips on sight reading: Before attempting to sight read, make sure that you can play the notes in the first position without looking at your fingers.

❶ Choose pieces that are below your current technical and playing abilities.
❷ Look at the complete score before playing; recognize the time and key signatures.
❸ Play through the pace no more than three times. After that, you are no longer sight reading.
❹ Keep your eyes on the score and play at a comfortable tempo.
❺ Don't stop if you make mistakes; keep going.
❻ Look ahead; try to read at least one note ahead; with practice you should be able to read easily *one measure* ahead.
❼ Read new material as often as possible; the key to becoming a good sight reader is daily practice.

Appendix

Memorization

Memorization is an essential skill for any musician. There are many different ways in which our brain memorizes and remembers music. The majority relies on muscle memory, in which we memorize by repeating until our fingers can play the music unconsciously. In this method, the fingers become the leaders and the brain is left in second place. This may be the fastest way to memorize music, but also the riskiest one as well. Why risky? Because in stressful situations, playing in a concert, exam, or competition, we become so cautious that we try to think about every note and finger movement, but in reality we are not really aware of what we are playing . Our fingers are set to autopilot mode, because that's the way we practiced, so the smallest mistake can easily destabilize us, and our fingers will not know where to go.

One way to prepare for this type of practice is to play the piece very slowly, thinking ahead of your fingers of the position and fingering of the coming note. Visualize the positing of your fingers and try to hear the sound of the notes before actually playing them.

The best possible way to practice and memorize is to use all of the methods mentioned above, and to make sure that your brain is always in the driver's seat, aware of every note and every finger movement.

Guitar Care

The best thing you can do to keep your guitar in good shape is to keep it in its case when you are not playing it. It is important to protect the guitar from extreme temperature changes and humidity. Wood expands when damp, and cracks if dried out.
To minimize the chance of damaging the instrument, it is recommended to:

1. Never subject the guitar to sudden extreme changes in temperature or humidity.
2. Never expose your guitar to direct sunlight!
3. Maintain the humidity level anywhere between 40% and 60%.
4. Never tune to a pitch higher than the standard A-440.
   If you are required to tune higher, tune back to normal pitch as soon as possible.
5. If you anticipate not playing the guitar for a long period of time, it is best to loosen the strings.

Congratulations! This marks the end of the book. By now you should have acquired all the required skills and techniques that enable you to move forward to the next level, i.e.: "Mastering the Classical Guitar, Book 1B". Following this series of books with great heart, determination, and a lot of practice, will put you on the right road to shape you into a well-rounded musician and guitarist.

"I worked hard. Anyone who works as hard as I did can achieve the same results."
-J. S. Bach-

Other Mel Bay Classical Guitar Books of Interest

20 Easy Classical Guitar Pieces for Kids (Eckels)

Francisco Tárrega and Ferdinando Carulli/A Student's Guide (Castle)

Carlos Barbosa-Lima: 30 Short Pieces for Guitar (Griggs/Barbosa-Lima)

Easy Classic Guitar Solos (M. Bay/Castle)

En Mode (S. Yates)

Etudes Mécaniques (S. Yates)

First Pieces for Classical Guitar by Louis Kohler (Griggs)

Graded Repertoire for Guitar Book One (S. Yates)

Jazz for Classic Guitar Made Easy (Vinitsky)

Jorge Morel: Solo Pieces for the Young Guitarist

Student Guitar Etudes (W. Bay)

Teaching Pieces for Classic Guitar (Lawry)

The Anna Magdalena Notebook for Classic Guitar (Tertocha)

Duets for Beginning Guitar (Boyd)

Graded Guitar Duos Volume 1 (Small/Torres)

Jorge Morel: Duet Pieces for the Young Guitarist

Latinas for Two (Montes)

Music of Bela Bartok: Easy Arrangements for Classic Guitar Duo (Crowley)

Folk Song Collection for Guitar Ensemble (Hirsh)

Jorge Morel: Quartet Pieces for the Young Guitarist

Music from Around the World for Guitar Ensemble (Miller)

Renaissance Music for Guitar Ensemble (Hirsh)

WWW.MELBAY.COM

37026355R00042

Made in the USA
Middletown, DE
21 February 2019